Can Cat Get Cod?

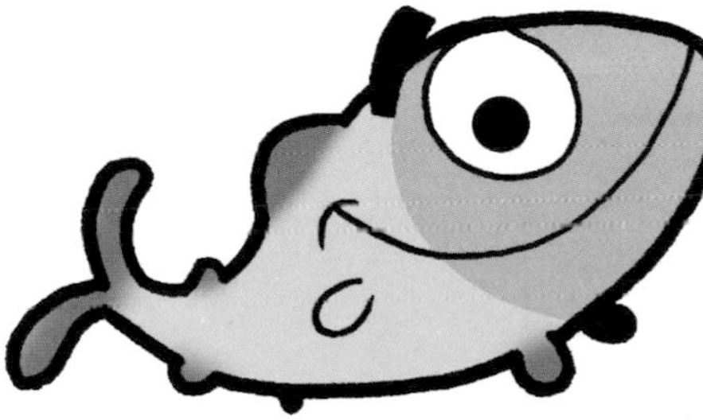

Writ ... oster
Illu ... vift

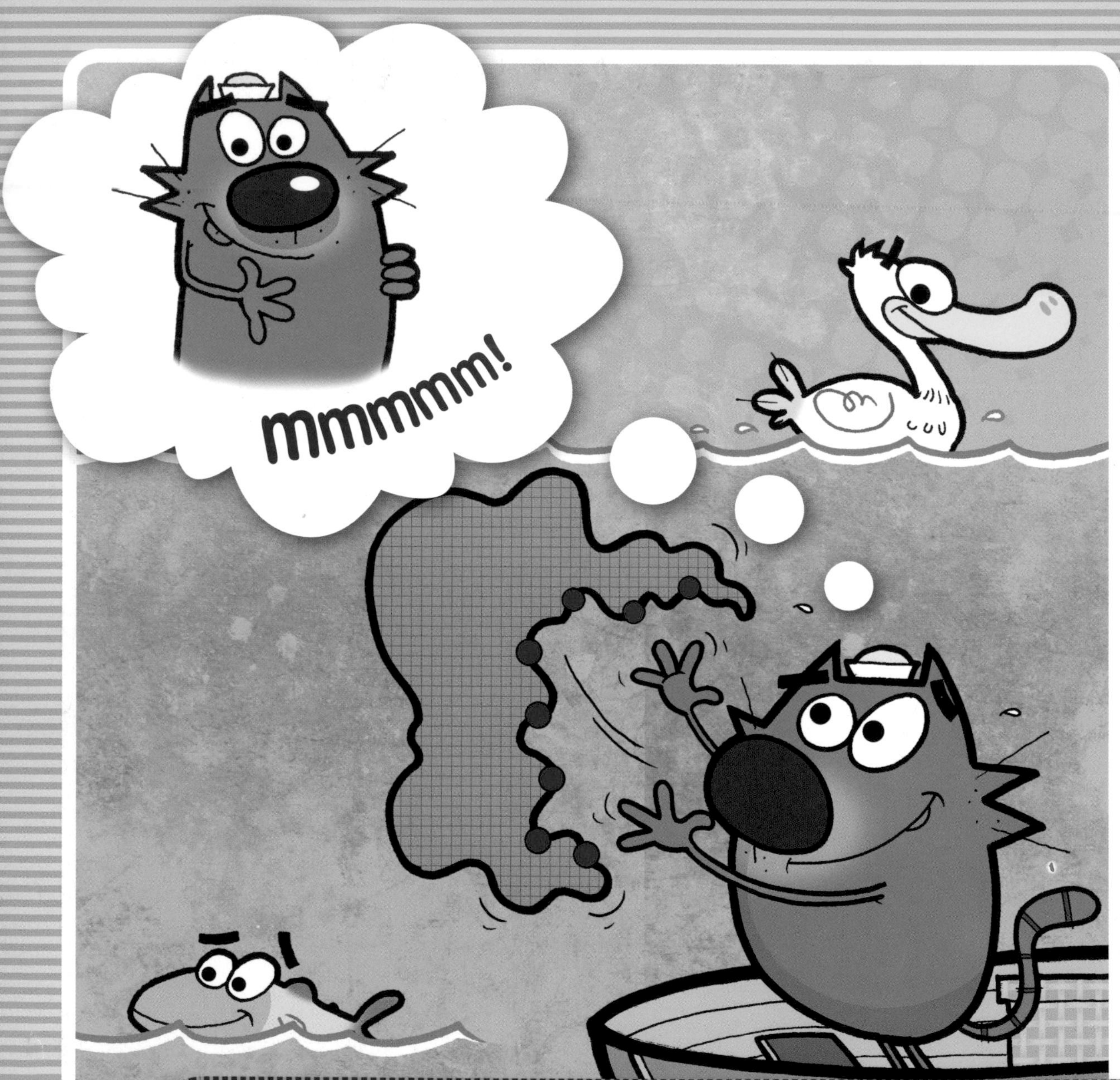

Can Cat get Cod in the net?

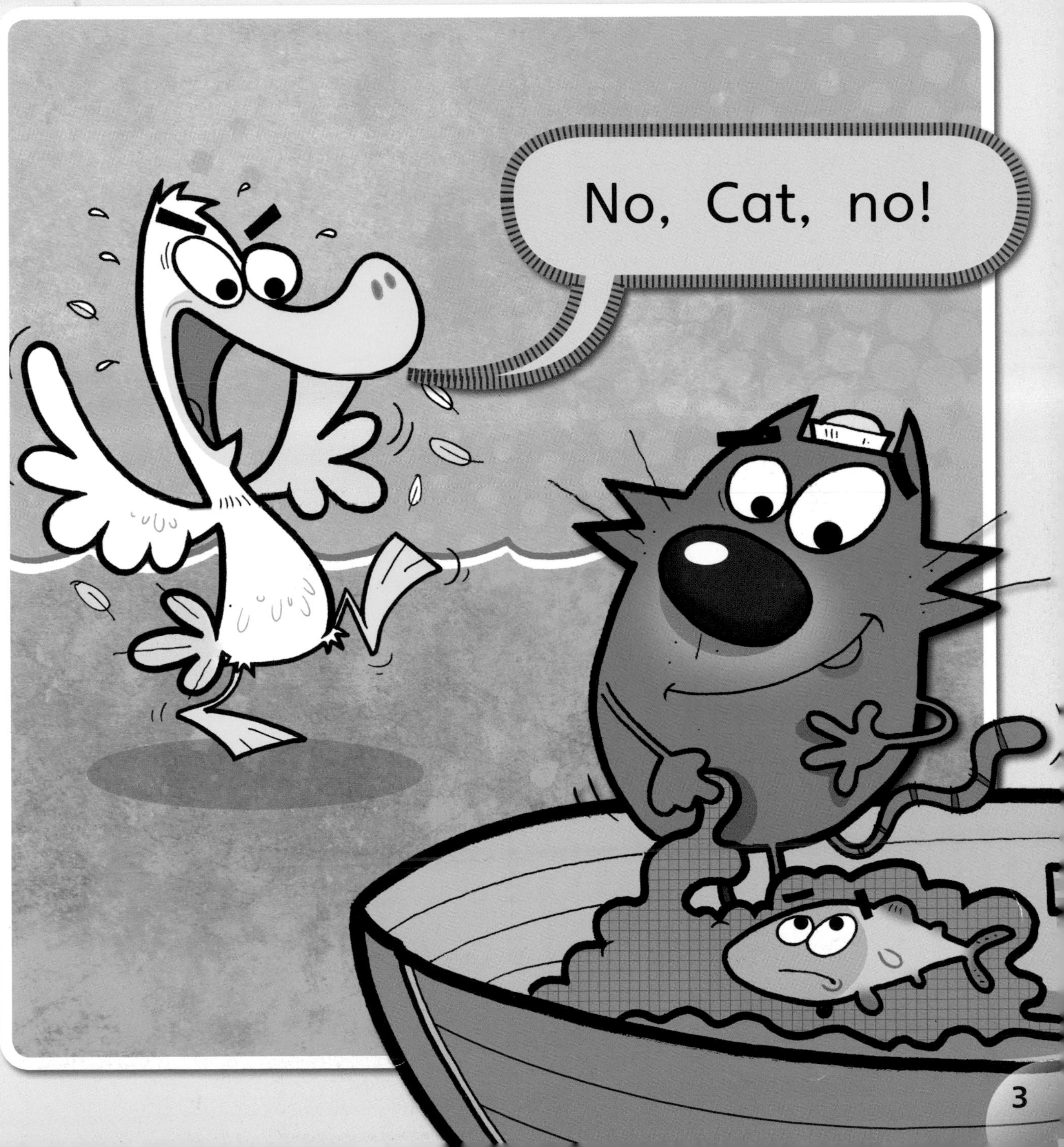
No, Cat, no!

Duck can tug the net.

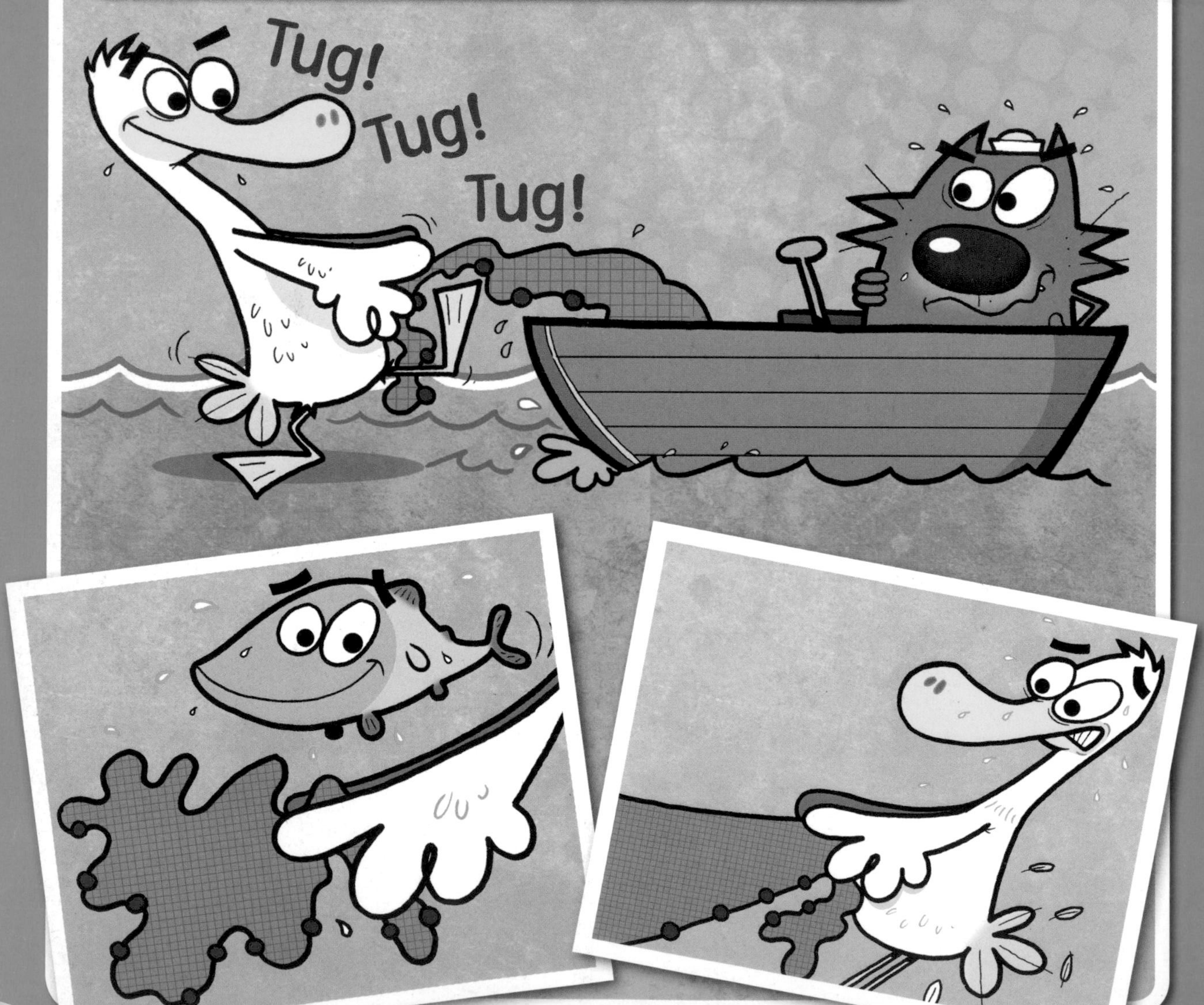

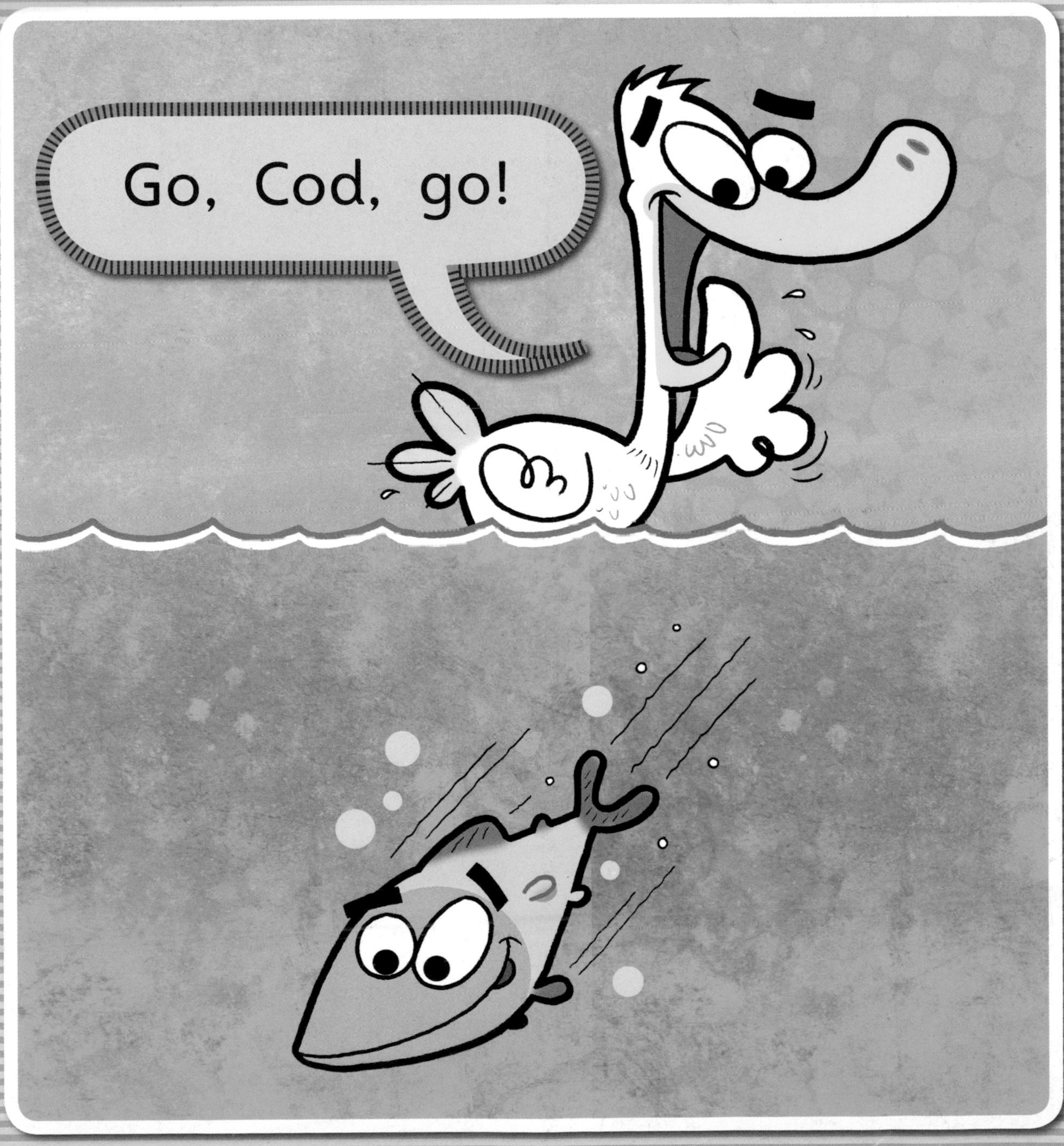
Go, Cod, go!

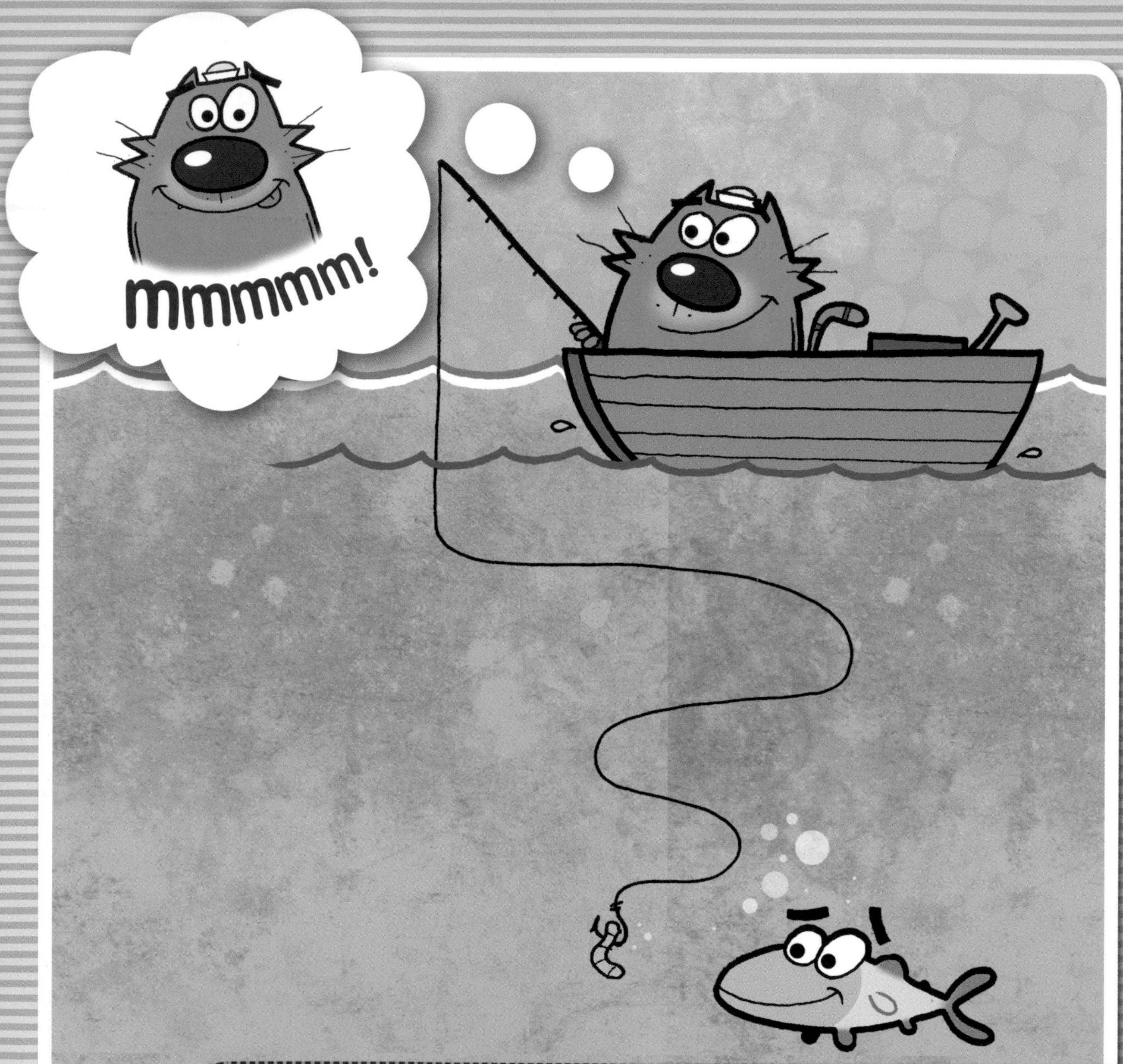

Can cat get Cod on a rod?

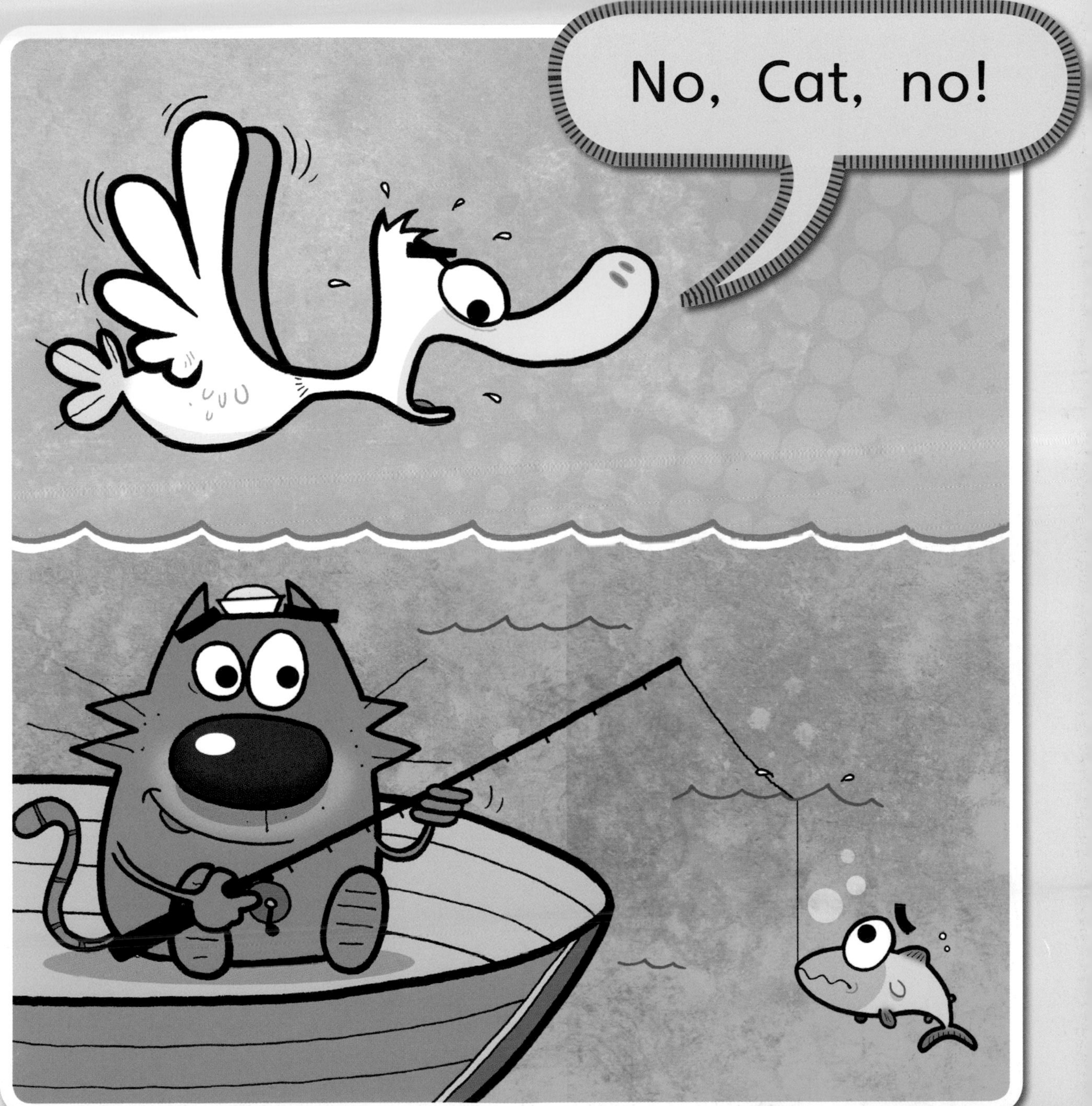
No, Cat, no!

Mad Duck can peck the rod.

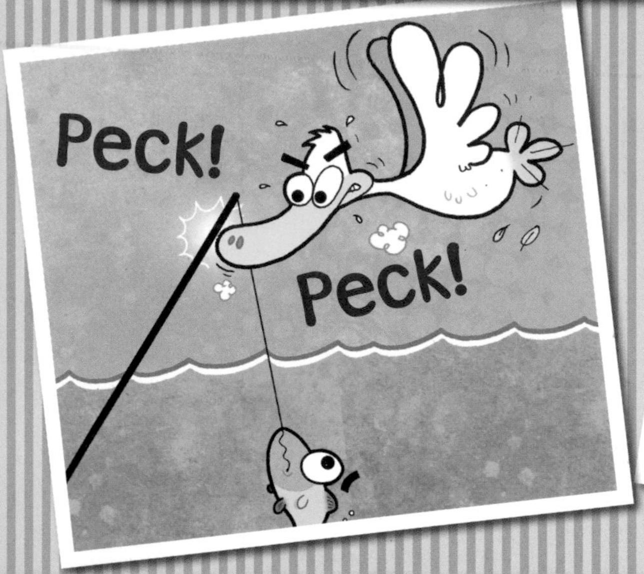

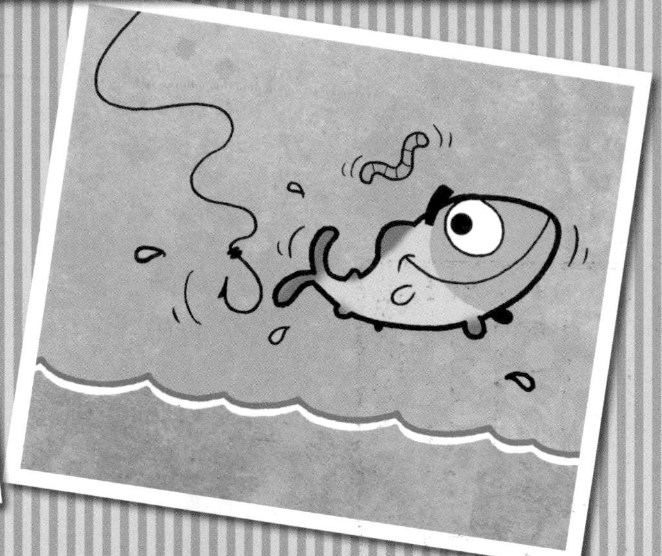

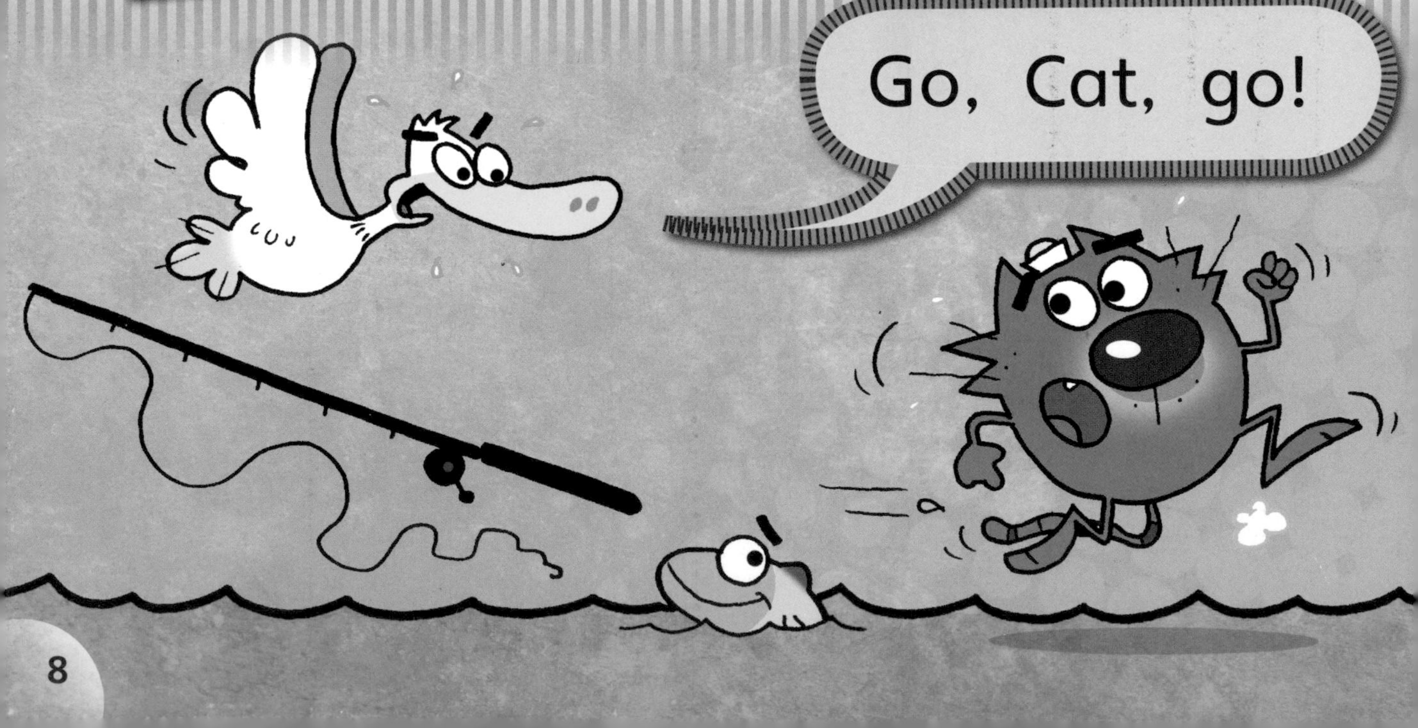